Light relief between grades

Spaß und Entspannung mit leichten Stücken für Klavier Zweiter Schwierigkeitsgrad

Plaisir et détente avec des pièces simples pour piano Niveau 2

Pam Wedgwood

FABER *ff* MUSIC

© 2008 by Faber Music Ltd
This edition first published in 2008
3 Queen Square London WC1N 3AU
Music processed by Don Sheppard
Cover design by Stik
Printed in England by Caligraving Ltd

ISBN10: 0-571-53124-5
EAN13: 978-0-571-53124-0

To buy Faber Music publications or to find out about the full range of titles available
please contact your local music retailer or Faber Music sales enquiries:

Faber Music Limited, Burnt Mill, Elizabeth Way, Harlow CM20 2HX
Tel: +44 (0)1279 82 89 82   Fax: +44 (0)1279 82 89 83
sales@fabermusic.com   fabermusic.com

Contents

1. Greased lightnin'

from *Grease*

Words and Music by
Warren Casey and Jim Jacobs

2. No matter what

from *Whistle down the wind*

Music by
Andrew Lloyd Webber

3. Respect, man!

Pam Wedgwood

4. What else can I do?

Pam Wedgwood

5. Thunderbirds are go

Words and Music by
Matthew Sargeant, Charles Simpson,
James Bourne, Thomas Fletcher and Barry Gray

6. You've got a friend

Words and Music by Carole King

Quite slow, with feeling ♩ = 100

7. Diamonds are forever

Words by Don Black
Music by John Barry

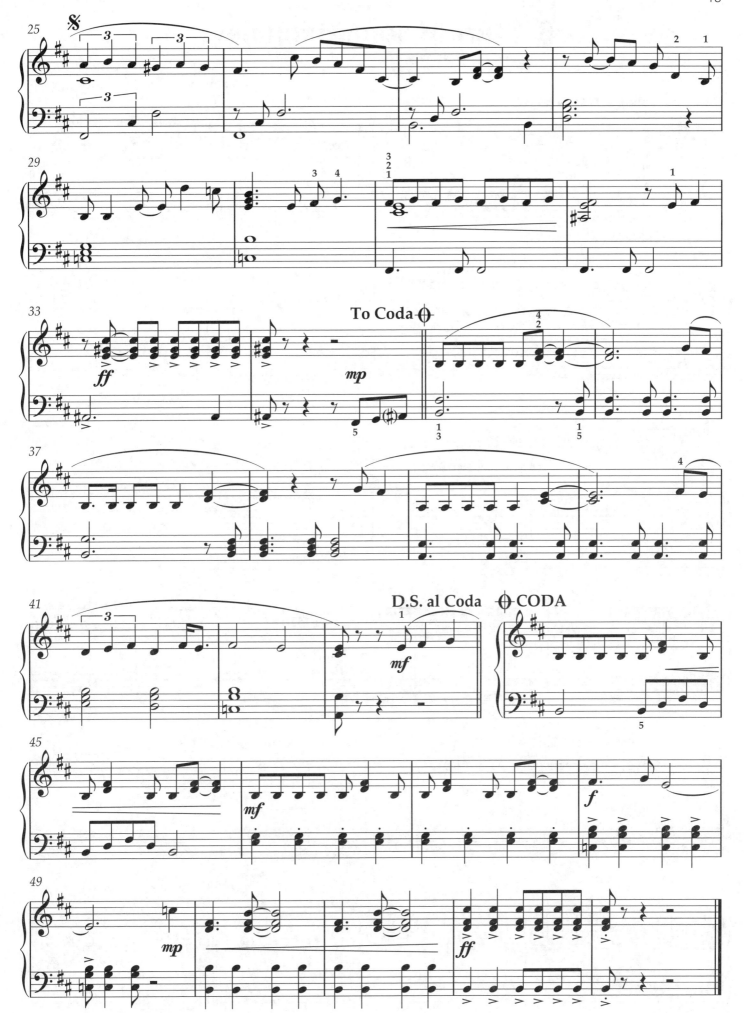

8. Start of something new

from *High School Musical*

Words and Music by
Matthew Gerrard and Robbie Nevil

9. You'll be in my heart

from *Tarzan*

Words and Music by Phillip Collins

10. Money, money, money

Words and Music by
Benny Andersson and Björn Ulvaeus

11. Back for good

Words and Music by Gary Barlow

Light relief between grades

Pamela Wedgwood

Tired of the same old exam pieces?
Looking for something to bridge the gap between grades?
Need a bit of light relief? *Up-Grade!* is for you!

Pam Wedgwood's inimitable, original style is guaranteed to breathe new life into your playing—
the varied pieces and duets in these bright new collections range from toe-tapping jazzy
numbers to more classical styles, all designed to ease you gently on towards the next grade.

Up-Grade! Piano Grades 0–1	ISBN 0-571-51737-4
More Up-Grade! Piano Grades 0–1	ISBN 0-571-51956-3
Up-Grade! Piano Grades 1–2	ISBN 0-571-51560-6
More Up-Grade! Piano Grades 1–2	ISBN 0-571-52420-6
Up-Grade! Piano Grades 2–3	ISBN 0-571-51561-4
More Up-Grade! Piano Grades 2–3	ISBN 0-571-52421-4
Up-Grade! Piano Grades 3–4	ISBN 0-571-51775-7
Up-Grade! Piano Grades 4–5	ISBN 0-571-51776-5
Up-Grade Pop! Piano Grades 0–1	ISBN 0-571-52474-5
Up-Grade Pop! Piano Grades 1–2	ISBN 0-571-52475-3
Up-Grade Pop! Piano Grades 2–3	ISBN 0-571-53124-5
Up-Grade Pop! Piano Grades 3–4	ISBN 0-571-53125-3
Up-Grade Jazz! Piano Grades 0–1	ISBN 0-571-52476-1
Up-Grade Jazz! Piano Grades 1–2	ISBN 0-571-52477-X
Up-Grade Jazz! Piano Grades 2–3	ISBN 0-571-53122-9
Up-Grade Jazz! Piano Grades 3–4	ISBN 0-571-53123-7
Up-Grade Christmas! Piano Grades 0–1	ISBN 0-571-52953-4
Up-Grade Christmas! Piano Grades 1–2	ISBN 0-571-52954-2

Lighten up and move on with Up-Grade!

To buy Faber Music publications or to find out about the full range of titles available
please contact your local music retailer or Faber Music sales enquiries:

Faber Music Ltd, Burnt Mill, Elizabeth Way, Harlow CM20 2HX
Tel: +44 (0) 1279 82 89 82   Fax: +44 (0) 1279 82 89 83
sales@fabermusic.com   fabermusic.com   expressprintmusic.com